Putting Together and Taking Apart

ADDITION AND SUBTRACTION

T E R C

Investigations in Number, Data, and Space®

Dale Seymour Publications®

Menlo Park, California

The *Investigations* curriculum was developed at TERC (formerly
Technical Education Research Centers) in collaboration with Kent State
University and the State University of New York at Buffalo. The work was
supported in part by National Science Foundation Grant No. ESI-9050210.
TERC is a nonprofit company working to improve mathematics and science
education. TERC is located at 2067 Massachusetts Avenue, Cambridge,
MA 02140.

This project was supported, in part,
by the
National Science Foundation
Opinions expressed are those of the authors
and not necessarily those of the Foundation

Managing Editor: Catherine Anderson
Series Editor: Beverly Cory
Manuscript Editor: Karen Becker
ESL Consultant: Nancy Sokol Green
Production/Manufacturing Director: Janet Yearian
Production/Manufacturing Coordinator: Amy Changar, Shannon Miller
Design Manager: Jeff Kelly
Design: Don Taka
Illustrations: Laurie Harden, Susan Jaekel, Meryl Treatner
Composition: Thomas Dvorak

This book is published by Dale Seymour Publications®, an imprint of
Addison Wesley Longman, Inc.

Dale Seymour Publications
2725 Sand Hill Road
Menlo Park, CA 94025
Customer Service: 800-872-1100

Order number DS43812
ISBN 1-57232-665-4
1 2 3 4 5 6 7 8 9 10-ML-01 00 99 98 97

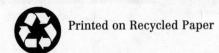
Printed on Recycled Paper

Contents

*Repeated-use sheet

*Repeated-use sheet

Weekly Log

Day Box

Monday, _____

Tuesday, _____

Wednesday, _____

Thursday, _____

Friday, _____

Weekly Log

Day Box

Monday, _____

Tuesday, _____

Wednesday, _____

Thursday, _____

Friday, _____

Weekly Log

Day Box

Monday, _____

Tuesday, _____

Wednesday, _____

Thursday, _____

Friday, _____

Weekly Log

Day Box

Monday, _____

Tuesday, _____

Wednesday, _____

Thursday, _____

Friday, _____

Weekly Log

Day Box

Monday, _____

Tuesday, _____

Wednesday, _____

Thursday, _____

Friday, _____

Weekly Log

Day Box

Monday, _____

Tuesday, _____

Wednesday, _____

Thursday, _____

Friday, _____

Weekly Log

Day Box

Monday, _____

Tuesday, _____

Wednesday, _____

Thursday, _____

Friday, _____

Story Problems, Set A

Solve these problems. Explain your strategies using pictures, numbers, or words.

1. A class of 29 students is going on a trip to the science museum. There are 12 adults going with them. How many people are going on the trip?

---

2. Next week other students will go to the science museum. There will be 39 students and 12 adults. How many people will go on this trip?

An Addition Story Problem

Write and solve a story problem about an addition
situation. Your story problem can be about anything
that you might see out your window at home. Show
your thinking using words, numbers, and pictures.
You may use the back of this sheet if necessary.

To the Family

An Addition Story Problem
Session 1

Math Content
Writing and solving addition story problems

Materials
Student Sheet 3
Pencil
Small objects to count (optional)

In class, we have been working on story problems, or word problems. For homework, your child will write a story problem about combining two things or two sets of things, using a subject she or he might see out a window at home, such as clouds, trucks, birds, people, or buildings.

Story Problems, Set B

Solve these problems. Explain your strategies using pictures, numbers, or words.

1. Yesterday at the park, I counted 39 pigeons. When a big dog walked by, 17 of them flew away. How many were still there?

_____

2. Today I went to the park again. I counted 39 pigeons. A big dog barked and 16 of them flew away. How many were still there?

A Subtraction Story Problem

Write and solve a story problem about a subtraction situation. Your story problem can be about anything that you might see out your window at home. Show your thinking using words, numbers, and pictures. You may use the back of this sheet if necessary.

To the Family

A Subtraction Story Problem
Session 2

Math Content
Writing and solving subtraction story problems

Materials
Student Sheet 5
Pencil
Small objects to count (optional)

In class, our work with story problems currently focuses on subtraction situations. For homework, your child will write a subtraction story problem on Student Sheet 5 about something he or she might see out a window at home. Your child will start with some amount, and then part of that amount will be lost, eaten, or taken away.

1. On Saturday, Kira and Jake counted animals in the park. They counted 23 pigeons and 37 squirrels. How many animals did they count?

2. Kira and Jake went for a walk. They counted 25 pigeons and 35 squirrels. How many animals did they count?

3. Kira and Jake fed bread crumbs to the birds in the pond. There were 16 ducks and 26 geese. How many birds were there?

4. One day, there were 26 ducks and 36 geese at the pond. How many birds were there?

5. On Monday there was a bicycle race in the park. There were 25 children and 18 adults in the race. How many people were in the race?

6. On Sunday, there was a kite-flying contest. There were 28 children and 15 adults flying kites. How many people were flying kites?

7. Kira planted 41 flowers in the fall. In the spring, 27 of them came up. How many flowers did not come up?

8. Kira's mother has 41 tomatoes that grew in her garden. She gave 17 of them to neighbors. Kira's family ate the rest. How many tomatoes did Kira's family eat?

9. In Jake's garden, 33 flowers came up. There are 15 tulips. The rest are daffodils. How many are daffodils?

10. In Kira's garden, 43 flowers came up. There are 25 tulips. The rest are daffodils. How many are daffodils?

11. In Kira's garden there were 45 daisies. Rabbits ate 29 of them. How many daisies are left?

12. Kira had 46 daisies in her garden. She picked 30 to give to her father. How many were left?

Story Problems, Set D

Solve these problems. Explain your strategies using pictures, numbers, or words.

1. Jake collects stamps. He had 32 stamps. His sister gave him some more. Now he has 48. How many did his sister give him?

---

2. Kira had 40 marbles. She gave some to her best friend. Now she has 28 marbles left. How many did she give to her friend?

Discussing Addition and Subtraction

Ask an adult in your household when he or she uses addition or subtraction. It might help to think about cooking, driving, shopping, or paying bills.

_____

_____

_____

_____

_____

_____

_____

_____

_____

_____

_____

_____

_____

To the Family

Discussing Addition and Subtraction

Sessions 3–4

Math Content
Identifying real-life addition and subtraction situations

Materials
Student Sheet 7
Pencil

In class, children have been making sense of addition and subtraction in meaningful ways. They have written and solved a variety of story problems. Tonight, your child will ask an adult at home about instances when he or she uses addition or subtraction, such as a job, cooking, driving, shopping, or paying bills.

1. Jake baked 24 cookies. Jake's mom baked some more. Then they had 48 cookies. How many did Jake's mom bake?

2. Jake and his mom baked 48 cookies. Jake ate 5 cookies, his sister ate 5 cookies, and his mom ate some. There are 35 cookies left. How many cookies did Jake's mom eat?

3. Kira earned 25¢ doing errands for her grandfather. She earned some more doing errands for her aunt. She earned 40¢ altogether. How much money did Kira's aunt pay her?

4. Jake earned 35¢ for cleaning the yard. His grandmother paid him to walk the dog. Now Jake has 50¢. How much did his grandmother pay him?

Problem Strategies

Here's the problem I am solving:

Here's how I solved it:

Here's the problem I am solving:

Here's how I solved it:

To the Family

Solving Story Problems

Sessions 5–6

Math Content

Interpreting, writing, and solving addition and subtraction story
problems

Materials

Student Sheet 8 with a problem from school attached
Student Sheet 9
Pencil
Small objects to count (optional)

In class, students have continued their work with addition and subtraction story problems. Your child will either complete a problem from class that has been stapled or glued onto Student Sheet 8 or write and solve an addition or subtraction story problem on Student Sheet 9.

Writing and Solving a Story Problem

Write and solve a story problem about either an addition or subtraction situation. Your story problem can be about anything that interests you. Show your thinking using words, numbers, and pictures. You may use the back of this sheet if necessary.

To the Family

Solving Story Problems

Sessions 5–6

Math Content

Interpreting, writing, and solving addition and subtraction story
  problems

Materials

Student Sheet 8 with a problem from school attached
Student Sheet 9
Pencil
Small objects to count (optional)

In class, students have continued their work with addition and subtraction story problems. Your child will either complete a problem from
class that has been stapled or glued onto Student Sheet 8 or write and
solve an addition or subtraction story problem on Student Sheet 9.

Problem Strategies

Here's the problem I am solving:

Here's how I solved it:

Here's the problem I am solving:

Here's how I solved it:

To the Family

Solving More Story Problems

Sessions 5–6

Math Content
Interpreting and solving addition and subtraction story problems

Materials
Student Sheet 8 with a story problem attached
Pencil
Small objects to count (optional)

In class, students have continued their work with addition and subtraction story problems. Tonight, your child will solve a problem from class, which will be stapled or glued onto Student Sheet 8.

Date

Side-by-Side 100 Charts

Name

1	2	3	4	5	6	7	8	9	10
11	12	13	14	15	16	17	18	19	20
21	22	23	24	25	26	27	28	29	30
31	32	33	34	35	36	37	38	39	40
41	42	43	44	45	46	47	48	49	50
51	52	53	54	55	56	57	58	59	60
61	62	63	64	65	66	67	68	69	70
71	72	73	74	75	76	77	78	79	80
81	82	83	84	85	86	87	88	89	90
91	92	93	94	95	96	97	98	99	100

1	2	3	4	5	6	7	8	9	10
11	12	13	14	15	16	17	18	19	20
21	22	23	24	25	26	27	28	29	30
31	32	33	34	35	36	37	38	39	40
41	42	43	44	45	46	47	48	49	50
51	52	53	54	55	56	57	58	59	60
61	62	63	64	65	66	67	68	69	70
71	72	73	74	75	76	77	78	79	80
81	82	83	84	85	86	87	88	89	90
91	92	93	94	95	96	97	98	99	100

1	2	3	4	5	6	7	8	9	10
11	12	13	14	15	16	17	18	19	20
21	22	23	24	25	26	27	28	29	30
31	32	33	34	35	36	37	38	39	40
41	42	43	44	45	46	47	48	49	50
51	52	53	54	55	56	57	58	59	60
61	62	63	64	65	66	67	68	69	70
71	72	73	74	75	76	77	78	79	80
81	82	83	84	85	86	87	88	89	90
91	92	93	94	95	96	97	98	99	100

1	2	3	4	5	6	7	8	9	10
11	12	13	14	15	16	17	18	19	20
21	22	23	24	25	26	27	28	29	30
31	32	33	34	35	36	37	38	39	40
41	42	43	44	45	46	47	48	49	50
51	52	53	54	55	56	57	58	59	60
61	62	63	64	65	66	67	68	69	70
71	72	73	74	75	76	77	78	79	80
81	82	83	84	85	86	87	88	89	90
91	92	93	94	95	96	97	98	99	100

How many cubes do you have in all?

How many more cubes do you need to finish another row of 10?

How far from 50 cubes are you?

How many cubes do you have? TAKE 10 cubes.

Now how many cubes do you have?

How many cubes do you need to add or take away so that you have 50 cubes in all?

Roll the number cubes again. TAKE double the number of cubes.

How many cubes do you have in all?

How many more cubes do you need to finish another row of 10?

How many cubes do you have? GIVE BACK 10 cubes. Now how many cubes do you have?

How many cubes do you have? TAKE 5 extra cubes. How many cubes do you have now?

Roll the number cubes again. TAKE double the number of cubes.

How many cubes do you have? TAKE another 10 cubes. How many cubes do you have now?

1	2	3	4	5	6	7	8	9	10
11	12	13	14	15	16	17	18	19	20
21	22	23	24	25	26	27	28	29	30
31	32	33	34	35	36	37	38	39	40
41	42	43	44	45	46	47	48	49	50
51	52	53	54	55	56	57	58	59	60
61	62	63	64	65	66	67	68	69	70
71	72	73	74	75	76	77	78	79	80
81	82	83	84	85	86	87	88	89	90
91	92	93	94	95	96	97	98	99	100

Name

Side-by-Side 100 Charts

1	2	3	4	5	6	7	8	9	10
11	12	13	14	15	16	17	18	19	20
21	22	23	24	25	26	27	28	29	30
31	32	33	34	35	36	37	38	39	40
41	42	43	44	45	46	47	48	49	50
51	52	53	54	55	56	57	58	59	60
61	62	63	64	65	66	67	68	69	70
71	72	73	74	75	76	77	78	79	80
81	82	83	84	85	86	87	88	89	90
91	92	93	94	95	96	97	98	99	100

Multiples-of-5 Cards

5	5	5	5
10	10	10	10
15	15	15	15
20	20	30	30
5	5	10	10

Get to 100

Materials: Multiples-of-5 number cubes (2) or set of Multiples-of-5 Cards, 100 chart (for each player), game piece (for each player), paper

Players: 2 to 3

How to Play

The object of the game is to reach 100 on the 100 chart.

1. Each player puts a game piece to the left of number 1.

2. Take turns. Roll the number cubes or draw two number cards and move that many spaces on the 100 chart.

3. Record your move on paper. For example, if your first roll is 5 and 15, write 5 + 15.

   If your next roll is 10 + 5, move that many spaces and add these numbers to your recording so that you have 5 + 15 + 10 + 5. Your game piece should be at 35.

4. Continue play, recording your moves each time.

5. You can use just one of the amounts on the number cubes or cards to land directly on 100.

6. When you reach 100, check your moves by adding all the numbers on your paper. If the sum does not equal 100, move your game piece back to the total number and continue play.

7. If the numbers do add to 100, move your game piece back and play again.

To the Family

Get to 100

Session 2

Math Content

Adding multiples of 5 and 10
Exploring how multiples of 5 and 10 relate to 100

Materials

Student Sheet 11 (to be cut apart into a deck)
Student Sheet 12
Two copies of a 100 chart
Scissors
Envelope or plastic bag for storing the deck of cards (optional)
A small object per player to use as a game piece
Paper
Pencil

In class, we have been working with the number 100. Students learned a game called Get to 100. For homework tonight, your child will play this game with someone at home and record at least two number sentences for getting to 100.

1	2	3	4	5	6	7	8	9	10
11	12	13	14	15	16	17	18	19	20
21	22	23	24	25	26	27	28	29	30
31	32	33	34	35	36	37	38	39	40
41	42	43	44	45	46	47	48	49	50
51	52	53	54	55	56	57	58	59	60
61	62	63	64	65	66	67	68	69	70
71	72	73	74	75	76	77	78	79	80
81	82	83	84	85	86	87	88	89	90
91	92	93	94	95	96	97	98	99	100

Unit Resource
Putting Together and Taking Apart

1	2	3	4	5	6	7	8	9	10
11	12	13	14	15	16	17	18	19	20
21	22	23	24	25	26	27	28	29	30
31	32	33	34	35	36	37	38	39	40
41	42	43	44	45	46	47	48	49	50
51	52	53	54	55	56	57	58	59	60
61	62	63	64	65	66	67	68	69	70
71	72	73	74	75	76	77	78	79	80
81	82	83	84	85	86	87	88	89	90
91	92	93	94	95	96	97	98	99	100

Pinching Paper Clips

1. I pinched _____ paper clips.
   There are _____ paper clips left in the box.
   Here's how I figured this out.

2. I pinched _____ paper clips.
   There are _____ paper clips left in the box.
   Here's how I figured this out.

3. I pinched _____ paper clips.
   There are _____ paper clips left in the box.
   Here's how I figured this out.

1. Jake has 73 pennies. When he gets 100 pennies he can trade them for $1. How many more pennies does Jake need?

2. Kira had 100 pennies. She spent 49 pennies on an apple. How many pennies does Kira have left?

3. Kira and Jake were playing Get to 100. Kira's marker was on 65. How far is Kira from 100?

4. In the game Get to 100, Jake's marker was on 35. How much more does Jake need to get to 100?

Investigation 2 • Resource
Putting Together and Taking Apart

5. Harris has a collection of 100 marbles. He gave some to his brother. Now he has 71 marbles left. How many did Harris give to his brother?

6. A bowl had 100 jelly beans. Jeffrey took a handful from the bowl. Now there are 82 jelly beans left in the bowl. How many did Jeffrey take?

7. Ebony and Simon want to make 100 paper hearts. Ebony has made 47 hearts and Simon has made 43 hearts. Have they made enough hearts?

If not, how many more should they make?

8. Laura had 27¢ in her pocket. Then she earned 25¢ for walking the dog and 45¢ for washing the dishes. How much money does Laura have now?

How much more money does Laura need to earn to have $1?

Pinching Objects

Fill a bag or bowl with 100 small objects such as beans, pennies, or buttons.

1. I pinched _____ _____ . There are _____ _____ left.
      (number) (object name)   (number) (object name)

Here's how I figured this out.

2. I pinched _____ _____ . There are _____ _____ left.
      (number) (object name)   (number) (object name)

Here's how I figured this out.

Optional: Take two or three pinches. Figure out how many are left.

To the Family

Pinching Objects

Sessions 3–4

Math Content

Figuring out combinations that equal 100 using addition and
  subtraction

Materials

Student Sheet 14
Pencil
100 small objects

In class, children have been playing a game called Pinching Paper Clips,
which focuses on combinations of numbers that make 100. Tonight,
your child will play a version of this game at home called Pinching
Objects. You child will need a bowl of 100 small things, such as maca-
roni, pennies, or dried beans, and Student Sheet 14 for recording. If
possible, save the collection of 100 items to use for future homework.

Pinching Paper Clips

1. I pinched _____ paper clips.
   There are _____ paper clips left in the box.
   Here's how I figured this out.

_____

2. I pinched _____ paper clips.
   There are _____ paper clips left in the box.
   Here's how I figured this out.

_____

3. I pinched _____ paper clips.
   There are _____ paper clips left in the box.
   Here's how I figured this out.

Problem Strategies

Here's the problem I am solving:

Here's how I solved it:

Here's the problem I am solving:

Here's how I solved it:

To the Family

Story Problems About 100

Sessions 5–6

Math Content

Figuring out combinations that equal 100 using addition and
  subtraction

Materials

Student Sheet 8 with a story problem about 100 from school attached
Pencil
Small objects to count (optional)

In class, we have continued to focus on number combinations that make
100. For homework, your child has chosen one story problem about 100
to solve and write about at home.

How Many Paper Clips?

Solve this problem. Explain your strategy using pictures, numbers, or words.

Franco has 63 paper clips and he needs to fill the box with 100 paper clips. How many more paper clips does he need to add to the box?

_____

Check your solution by solving the problem in a different way. Explain the strategy you used to check.

Writing and Solving Story Problems About 100

Use your collection of 100 small objects to write and solve a story problem about 100. Show your thinking using words, numbers, and pictures. You may use the back of this sheet if necessary.

To the Family

Writing and Solving Story Problems About 100

Session 7

Math Content

Figuring out combinations that equal 100 using operations (particularly addition and subtraction) flexibly

Materials

Student Sheet 16
Pencil
Collection of 100 small objects

Your child's homework is to write and solve a story problem about the collection of 100 small objects you assembled for playing Pinching Objects. The problem might describe a turn of Pinching Objects (for example, "I pinched 26 paper clips. How many were left?"), or it might have a completely different format. Either format is fine as long as the problem is about 100 objects.

Cover-Up Recording Sheet

Total Number	Number Not Covered	Number Covered
_____	_____	_____
_____	_____	_____
_____	_____	_____
_____	_____	_____
_____	_____	_____
_____	_____	_____
_____	_____	_____
_____	_____	_____
_____	_____	_____

© Dale Seymour Publications®

Investigation 3 • Session 1
Putting Together and Taking Apart

Story Problems, Set F

Solve these problems. Explain your strategies using pictures, numbers, or words.

1. Mrs. Lee had 46 goldfish in her pet store. She sold some of the goldfish. Now she has 25 left. How many goldfish did Mrs. Lee sell?

2. Mrs. Lee had 46 mice in her pet store. She sold some of the mice. Now she has 27 mice left. How many mice did she sell?

Cover-Up Recording Sheet

Total Number	Number Not Covered	Number Covered
_____	_____	_____
_____	_____	_____
_____	_____	_____
_____	_____	_____
_____	_____	_____
_____	_____	_____
_____	_____	_____
_____	_____	_____
_____	_____	_____

To the Family

Cover-Up

Session 2

Math Content
Finding a missing part when the total and one part are known

Materials
Student Sheet 17
Pencil
12–25 small objects
A piece of paper or cloth for covering the objects

In class, we have been playing games and solving problems about missing parts. For example, "We have 15 paper clips altogether. I hid some under a piece of paper. There are 5 paper clips showing that are *not* hidden under the paper. How many are under the paper?"

For homework, your child will play a game called Cover-Up with someone at home, Your child will need between 12 and 25 small objects such as beans, pennies, or paper clips. To begin, both players must know the total number of objects. Player 1 covers up some of the objects with a cloth or piece of paper while Player 2 looks away. Then Player 2 figures out how many objects are under the paper or cloth, using the number of objects that are showing. Your child will record the results of the games you play on Student Sheet 17.

Cover-Up Recording Sheet

Total Number	Number Not Covered	Number Covered
_____	_____	_____
_____	_____	_____
_____	_____	_____
_____	_____	_____
_____	_____	_____
_____	_____	_____
_____	_____	_____
_____	_____	_____
_____	_____	_____

1. Jake and Kira were playing Cover-Up. They had 45 buttons. Jake covered some up. Kira could still see 28. How many buttons did Jake cover?

2. Kira had a pile of 28 buttons. Jake put some more buttons in the pile. Then they had 43 buttons. How many buttons did Jake put in the pile?

3. Kira and Jake have 50¢. If they share a soda that costs 29¢, how much money will they have left?

4. Kira bought a soda for 29¢ and Jake bought a juice for 25¢. How much money did they spend?

5. Jake had 25¢. He found 11¢ in his room. He earned 40¢ more for shoveling snow. How much does he have now?

6. Kira had 76¢. She bought some apples and got 25¢ change. How much did the apples cost?

7. Kira collects shells. She found 25 of them on the beach. Her grandfather gave her some more. Now she has 41 shells. How many shells did her grandfather give her?

8. Jake had 35¢ in his pocket. He dropped 17¢ when it fell through a hole in his pocket. How much money does Jake have now?

9. Kira wants to buy a book that costs $1. She has 72¢. How much more does she need?

10. Jake took $1 to the store. He bought an eraser for 39¢ and a pencil for 35¢. How much change did he get?

$$35 + 27 = \underline{\hspace{2cm}}$$

$$63 - 18 = \underline{\hspace{2cm}}$$

$$41 + \underline{\hspace{2cm}} = 66$$

$$52 - \underline{\hspace{2cm}} = 31$$

$$25 + 57 = \underline{\hspace{2cm}}$$

$$41 - 13 = \underline{\hspace{2cm}}$$

$$16 + \underline{\hspace{2cm}} = 72$$

$$56 - \underline{\hspace{2cm}} = 38$$

$$\underline{\hspace{2cm}} + 13 = 70$$

$$100 - \underline{\hspace{2cm}} = 85$$

Cover-Up Recording Sheet

Total Number	Number Not Covered	Number Covered
_____	_____	_____
_____	_____	_____
_____	_____	_____
_____	_____	_____
_____	_____	_____
_____	_____	_____
_____	_____	_____
_____	_____	_____
_____	_____	_____

To the Family

Finding-the-Missing-Part Activities

Sessions 3–5

Math Content
Finding the missing part when the total and one part are known

In class, we have continued to work on games and problems about finding missing parts. During Choice Time, students have worked on three activities: Cover-Up, Solving Story Problems, and Creating Story Problems. Your child will be assigned one to three of these activities over the next few days. Following is the activity for today's homework:

■ **Cover-Up**

Materials
Student Sheet 17
Pencil
12–15 small objects
A piece of paper or cloth

Your child will continue to play Cover-Up with someone at home. You might try playing with a different number than the last time.

Problem Strategies

Here's the problem I am solving:

Here's how I solved it:

Here's the problem I am solving:

Here's how I solved it:

To the Family

Finding-the-Missing-Part Activities

Sessions 3–5

Math Content

Finding the missing part when the total and one part are known

In class, we have continued to work on games and problems about finding missing parts. During Choice Time, students have worked on three activities: Cover-Up, Solving Story Problems, and Creating Story Problems. Your child will be assigned one to three of these activities over the next few days. Following is the activity for today's homework:

■ Solving Story Problems

Materials
Student Sheet 8 with a story problem from school attached
Pencil
Small objects to count (optional)

Your child will bring home a story problem to solve and write about.

Problem Strategies

Here's the problem I am solving:

Here's how I solved it:

Here's the problem I am solving:

Here's how I solved it:

To the Family

Finding-the-Missing-Part Activities

Sessions 3–5

Math Content
Finding the missing part when the total and one part are known

In class, we have continued to work on games and problems about finding missing parts. During Choice Time, students have worked on three activities: Cover-Up, Solving Story Problems, and Creating Story Problems. Your child will be assigned one to three of these activities over the next few days. Following is the activity for today's homework:

■ **Solving Story Problems**

   Materials
   Student Sheet 8 with an equation from school attached
   Pencil
   Small objects to count (optional)

   Your child will bring home an equation card from school, stapled or glued to Student Sheet 8. In the space provided for a solution, your child will write a story problem that matches the equation.

Ways to Make 100

Make 100 in as many ways as you can. Think
of at least five ways. You might want to use your
collection of 100 small objects. Make sure to show your
solutions and how you reached them!

To the Family

Ways to Make 100

Session 2

Math Content

Figuring out combinations that equal 100 using operations (particularly
addition and subtraction) flexibly

Materials

Student Sheet 19
Pencil
100 small objects to count (optional)

In class, we are exploring 100 and how other numbers relate to it. For
homework, your child will write at least five ways to make 100 using
any operation (addition, subtraction, multiplication, division) and record
the equations on Student Sheet 19.

Cover-Up Recording Sheet

Total Number	Number Not Covered	Number Covered
_____	_____	_____
_____	_____	_____
_____	_____	_____
_____	_____	_____
_____	_____	_____
_____	_____	_____
_____	_____	_____
_____	_____	_____
_____	_____	_____

Ways to Make $1

Make $1 in as many ways as you can using nickels, dimes, and quarters. Record your answer using numbers, pictures, and/or words.

To the Family

Ways to Make $1

Sessions 3–4

Math Content

Finding combinations of numbers that add up to 100
Counting by 5's and 10's
Exploring and adding multiples of 5 and 10

Materials

Student Sheet 20
Pencil
Nickels, dimes, and quarters; or you and your child could make small
  paper coins (optional)

In class, students have been working with 100. One way we have been
exploring 100 is through the concept of money. For homework, your
child will find as many possible coin combinations that equal $1 as she
or he can using nickels, dimes, and quarters.

Comparing Story Problems

Show how you solved the problem. Use words, pictures, or numbers.

1. Kira and Jake are playing marbles. Kira has 40 marbles and Jake has 26. How many more marbles does Kira have than Jake?

2. Jake played marbles with some friends. He started with 26 marbles. At the end of the game he had 48 marbles. How many marbles did Jake win?

A Comparing Story Problem

Think about a situation where you might compare two amounts. Write and solve a story problem that compares two numbers. Show your thinking using words, numbers, and pictures.

To the Family

A Comparing Story Problem

Session 1

Math Content

Using addition and/or subtraction to compare two amounts

Materials

Student Sheet 22
Pencil
Small objects to count (optional)

In class, we are working on problems that compare two amounts. For example, "Kira has 40 marbles and Jake has 26. How many more marbles does Kira have than Jake?" Some people see this problem as subtraction and take 26 away from 40. Other people see it as addition and add from 26 up to 40. For homework, your child will think of a real situation where he or she might compare two amounts, write a story problem about it, and solve it on Student Sheet 22.

1	2	3	4	5	6	7	8	9	10
11	12	13	14	15	16	17	18	19	20
21	22	23	24	25	26	27	28	29	30
31	32	33	34	35	36	37	38	39	40
41	42	43	44	45	46	47	48	49	50
51	52	53	54	55	56	57	58	59	60
61	62	63	64	65	66	67	68	69	70
71	72	73	74	75	76	77	78	79	80
81	82	83	84	85	86	87	88	89	90
91	92	93	94	95	96	97	98	99	100

Unit Resource
Putting Together and Taking Apart

Capture 5 Recording Sheet

Record your starting number, the changes you use, and your ending number for each move, like this:

$$16 + 10 + 10 - 2 = 34$$

_____

_____

_____

_____

_____

_____

_____

_____

_____

_____

Change Cards (1–3)

+1	+1	+1	+1
–1	–1	–1	–1
+2	+2	+2	+2
–2	–2	–2	–2
+3	+3	–3	–3

Change Cards (10–30)

+10	+10	+10	+10
−10	−10	−10	−10
+20	+20	+20	+20
−20	−20	−20	−20
+30	+30	−30	−30

1. Kira has 36 marbles and Jake has 58 marbles. How many more marbles does Kira have than Jake?

2. Kira and Jake went to the post office to buy three stamps. Each stamp cost 32¢. How much money did they need?

3. Kira and Jake want to buy three apples. Each apple costs 33¢. Kira has 44¢ and Jake has 35¢. Do they have enough money to buy three apples?

Will they have any money left or will they need more? How much?

4. Jake is making a birthday cake for his mom. She will be 42 years old. Jake only has 27 candles. How many more candles does he need?

5. The pet store had a large tank filled with 100 goldfish. Kira bought 23 and Jake bought 19. How many goldfish were left at the pet store?

6. Jake and his dad blew up 60 balloons for his mom's party. Jake's cat Roo popped 23 balloons with his claws. How many balloons were left?

7. Jake and Kira each collected cans for recycling. Jake collected 48 cans in all. He collected 12 more than Kira. How many cans did Kira collect?

8. Two classes of students went to the park. There was a total of 64 students. One class had 33 students. How many students were in the other class?

Capture 5

Materials: 100 chart, deck of Change Cards, 12 markers of one color, game piece for each player, paper

Players: Two players or two teams

How to Play

The object of the game is to collect 5 game markers.

1. Place 12 markers on the 100 chart, so each marker is on a different number. Deal 5 Change Cards to each player or team and place the remaining cards face down. Players put their game pieces anywhere on the 100 chart.

2. On a turn, move your game piece using any combination of your Change Cards to land on a square with a marker. You can use any number of cards from 1 to 5.

3. If you land exactly on a square with a marker, capture it by taking it off the board. You can only capture one marker during a turn, and it must be the last square you land on.

4. Record your moves in an equation. If you begin on 45, and use the cards: +2, +10, +3, you record: $45 + 2 + 10 + 3 = 60$.

5. Place the Change Cards you used face down in a discard pile. Take cards from the top of the deck to replace them. If the deck of Change Cards is used up, shuffle the discard pile and turn it face down again.

6. The first player or team to capture 5 markers wins.

To the Family

Capture 5

Sessions 2–3

Math Content
Adding, subtracting, comparing two numbers
Working with 1's and 10's

Materials
100 chart (game board)
Student Sheet 23
Student Sheets 24 and 25 (to be cut apart into a deck)
Student Sheet 26
Pencil
Scissors
An envelope or plastic bag for storing Change Cards (optional
12 small like objects to use as game board markers (objects to place on
    numbers on the 100 chart and capture)
1 game piece for each player (small objects that are different from each
    other and from the markers)

One way we have been thinking about comparing two numbers is thinking about the distance between them. We have been playing a game
called Capture 5, which encourages children to think about the distance
between markers on a 100 chart. For homework, your child will play
Capture 5 with someone at home. Your child will want to keep these
materials in a safe place, as she or he will be playing again for homework later in this unit.

1	2	3	4	5	6	7	8	9	10
11	12	13	14	15	16	17	18	19	20
21	22	23	24	25	26	27	28	29	30
31	32	33	34	35	36	37	38	39	40
41	42	43	44	45	46	47	48	49	50
51	52	53	54	55	56	57	58	59	60
61	62	63	64	65	66	67	68	69	70
71	72	73	74	75	76	77	78	79	80
81	82	83	84	85	86	87	88	89	90
91	92	93	94	95	96	97	98	99	100

Unit Resource
Putting Together and Taking Apart

Change Cards (1-3)

+1	+1	+1	+1
−1	−1	−1	−1
+2	+2	+2	+2
−2	−2	−2	−2
+3	+3	−3	−3

Change Cards (10–30)

+10	+10	+10	+10
−10	−10	−10	−10
+20	+20	+20	+20
−20	−20	−20	−20
+30	+30	−30	−30

Capture 5 Recording Sheet

Record your starting number, the changes you use, and your ending number for each move, like this:

$$16 + 10 + 10 - 2 = 34$$

_____

_____

_____

_____

_____

_____

_____

_____

_____

_____

_____

To the Family

Capture 5

Sessions 2–3

Math Content

Adding, subtracting, comparing two numbers
Working with 1's and 10's

Materials

100 chart (game board)
Student Sheet 23
Student Sheets 24 and 25 (to be cut apart into a deck)
Student Sheet 26
Pencil
Scissors
An envelope or plastic bag for storing Change Cards (optional
12 small like objects to use as game board markers (objects to place on
   numbers on the 100 chart and capture)
1 game piece for each player (small objects that are different from each
   other and from the markers)

One way we have been thinking about comparing two numbers is thinking about the distance between them. We have been playing a game
called Capture 5, which encourages children to think about the distance
between markers on a 100 chart. For homework, your child will play
Capture 5 with someone at home. Your child will want to keep these
materials in a safe place, as she or he will be playing again for homework later in this unit.

Capture 5 Recording Sheet

Record your starting number, the changes you use, and your ending number for each move, like this:

$$16 + 10 + 10 - 2 = 34$$

_____

_____

_____

_____

_____

_____

_____

_____

_____

_____

1. Kira had 48¢ in her pocket. Her big brother gave her 25¢ for running an errand. Now how much does she have?

2. Jake has 23¢ in his pocket. Kira has 25¢ more than Jake. How much money does Kira have?

3. Kira and Jake were riding the bus. They counted 33 people on the bus. More people got on. Now there are 62 people on the bus. How many more people got on the bus?

4. There are 53 people on the bus. There are 27 adults. The rest are children. How many are children?

5. Kira wants to buy a pen. She sees a red one that costs 48¢. She also sees one with sparkles for 65¢. How much more does the one with sparkles cost?

6. Kira chooses a pen with stars. She pays for it with three quarters. She gets 10¢ change. How much does the pen cost?

Problem Strategies

Here's the problem I am solving:

Here's how I solved it:

Here's the problem I am solving:

Here's how I solved it:

To the Family

Solving Story Problems

Sessions 4–5

Math Content

Interpreting and solving addition and subtraction situations

Materials

Student Sheet 8 with one or two problems attached
Pencil
Small objects to count

In class, students have been solving a variety of addition and subtraction story problems. For homework, your child will bring home one or two problems he or she has not completed yet. Your child will solve the problem(s) and record his or her method of solving it (them) on Student Sheet 8.

Writing and Solving a Story Problem

Write and solve a story problem about either an addition or subtraction situation. Your story problem can be about anything that interests you. Show your thinking using words, numbers, and pictures. You may use the back of this sheet if necessary.

To the Family

Solving More Story Problems

Sessions 4–5

Math Content

Writing, illustrating, and solving story problems for a variety of kinds of situations (addition, subtraction, comparing)

Materials

Student Sheet 9 or Student Sheet 22
Pencil
Small objects to count

For tonight's homework, your child will write, illustrate, and solve a story problem. We will collect students' story problems and make them into a book, which we can then use for further work on story problems. You child will bring home a student sheet that matches the type of story problem she or he chooses to write.

A Comparing Story Problem

Think about a situation where you might compare two amounts. Write and solve a story problem that compares two numbers. Show your thinking using words, numbers, and pictures.

To the Family

Solving More Story Problems

Sessions 4–5

Math Content

Writing, illustrating, and solving story problems for a variety of kinds of situations (addition, subtraction, comparing)

Materials

Student Sheet 9 or Student Sheet 22
Pencil
Small objects to count

For tonight's homework, your child will write, illustrate, and solve a story problem. We will collect students' story problems and make them into a book, which we can then use for further work on story problems. You child will bring home a student sheet that matches the type of story problem she or he chooses to write.

Capture 5 Equations

1. Linda's marker was on 21 and she captured a marker on 47. She wrote this equation: 21 + 2 + 3 + 1 + 20 = 47. How many spaces did Linda move? Explain how you figured this out.

Rewrite Linda's equation to show how far she moved:
21 + _____ = 47

2. Ping's marker was on 58 and he captured a marker on 92. He wrote this equation: 58 + 2 + 30 + 2 = 92. How many spaces did Ping move? Explain how you figured this out.

Rewrite Ping's equation to show how far he moved: _____

3. Jeffrey's marker was on 9 and he captured a marker on 37. He wrote this equation: 9 + 20 + 3 + 2 + 3 = 37. How many spaces did Jeffrey move? Explain how you figured this out.

Rewrite Jeffrey's equation to show how far he moved: _____

Capture 5 Recording Sheet

Record your starting number, the changes you use, and your ending number for each move, like this:

$$16 + 10 + 10 - 2 = 34$$

_____

_____

_____

_____

_____

_____

_____

_____

_____

_____

_____

To the Family

More Capture 5

Session 6

Math Content
Adding, subtracting, comparing two numbers
Working with 1's and 10's

Materials
100 chart (game board)
Deck of Change Cards
Student Sheet 23 or paper to make a recording sheet
Student Sheet 26
Pencil
12 small like objects to use as game board markers (objects to place on numbers on the 100 chart and capture)
1 game piece for each player (small objects that are different from each other and from the markers)

We have been developing strategies for playing the game Capture 5. For homework, you child will play Capture 5 with someone at home. Your child should have all the necessary materials at home already, from the last time he or she played this game for homework.

Capture 5 Recording Sheet

Record your starting number, the changes you use, and your ending number for each move, like this:

$$16 + 10 + 10 - 2 = 34$$

_____

_____

_____

_____

_____

_____

_____

_____

_____

_____

© Dale Seymour Publications®

Investigation 5 • Sessions 2–3
Putting Together and Taking Apart

Alphabet Addition

Make five words and use the code in the chart below to figure out how much each word is worth. Show how you figured out how much each word is worth.

All consonants are worth 5, except for J, Q, V, W, X, and Z.

All vowels are worth 10.

J, Q, V, W, X, and Z are worth 15.

A = 10	G = 5	M = 5	S = 5	Y = 5
B = 5	H = 5	N = 5	T = 5	Z = 15
C = 5	I = 10	O = 10	U = 10	
D = 5	J = 15	P = 5	V = 15	
E = 10	K = 5	Q = 15	W = 15	
F = 5	L = 5	R = 5	X = 15	

To the Family

Alphabet Addition

Session 7

Math Content

Developing strategies for adding multiples of 5 and 10

Materials

Student Sheet 28
Pencil
Small objects or coins to count

In class, we have been developing strategies for adding and subtracting, particularly using multiples of 5 and 10. For tonight's homework, your child will use the values assigned to each letter of the alphabet on Student Sheet 28 to figure out how much different words are worth.

How Far?

1. How far is it from 38 to 65? How do you know?
   Explain your thinking using words and numbers.

2. How far is it from 52 to 29? How do you know?
   Explain your thinking using words and numbers.

Tens Go Fish

Materials: Deck of Number Cards 0–10 (four of each) with the wild cards removed

Players: 3 to 4

How to Play

The object of the game is to get two cards that total 10.

1. Each player is dealt five cards. The rest of the cards are placed face down in the center of the table.

2. If you have any pairs of cards that total 10, put them down in front of you and replace those cards with cards from the deck.

3. Take turns. On a turn, ask <u>one</u> other player for a card that will go with a card in your hand to make 10.

4. If you get a card that makes 10, put the pair of cards down. Take one card from the deck. Your turn is over.

   If you do not get a card that makes 10, take the top card from the deck. Your turn is over.

   If the card you take from the deck makes 10 with a card in your hand, put the pair down and take another card.

5. If there are no cards left in your hand but still cards in the deck, you take two cards.

6. The game is over when there are no more cards.

7. At the end of the game, make a list of the number pairs you made.

Close to 20

Materials: Deck of Number Cards 0–10 (four of each) with the wild cards removed; Close to 20 Score Sheet; counters

Players: 2 to 3

How to Play

The object of the game is to choose three cards that total as close to 20 as possible.

1. Deal five cards to each player.

2. Take turns. Use any three of your cards to make a total that is as close to 20 as possible.

3. Write these numbers and the total on the Close to 20 Score Sheet.

4. Find your score. The score for the round is the difference between the total and 20. For example, if you choose 8 + 7 + 3, your total is 18 and your score for the round is 2.

5. After you record your score, take that many counters.

6. Put the cards you used in a discard pile and deal three new cards to each player. If you run out of cards before the end of the game, shuffle the discard pile and use those cards again.

7. After five rounds, total your score and count your counters. These two numbers should be the same. The player with the lowest score and the fewest counters is the winner.

Close to 20 Score Sheet

PLAYER 1   SCORE

Round 1: _____ + _____ + _____ = _____   _____

Round 2: _____ + _____ + _____ = _____   _____

Round 3: _____ + _____ + _____ = _____   _____

Round 4: _____ + _____ + _____ = _____   _____

Round 5: _____ + _____ + _____ = _____   _____

                                         TOTAL SCORE   _____

PLAYER 2   SCORE

Round 1: _____ + _____ + _____ = _____   _____

Round 2: _____ + _____ + _____ = _____   _____

Round 3: _____ + _____ + _____ = _____   _____

Round 4: _____ + _____ + _____ = _____   _____

Round 5: _____ + _____ + _____ = _____   _____

                                         TOTAL SCORE   _____

Close to 20 Score Sheet

PLAYER 1   SCORE

Round 1: _____ + _____ + _____ = _____   _____

Round 2: _____ + _____ + _____ = _____   _____

Round 3: _____ + _____ + _____ = _____   _____

Round 4: _____ + _____ + _____ = _____   _____

Round 5: _____ + _____ + _____ = _____   _____

                              TOTAL SCORE   _____

PLAYER 2   SCORE

Round 1: _____ + _____ + _____ = _____   _____

Round 2: _____ + _____ + _____ = _____   _____

Round 3: _____ + _____ + _____ = _____   _____

Round 4: _____ + _____ + _____ = _____   _____

Round 5: _____ + _____ + _____ = _____   _____

                              TOTAL SCORE   _____

Close to 20 Score Sheet

PLAYER 1   SCORE

Round 1: _____ + _____ + _____ = _____   _____

Round 2: _____ + _____ + _____ = _____   _____

Round 3: _____ + _____ + _____ = _____   _____

Round 4: _____ + _____ + _____ = _____   _____

Round 5: _____ + _____ + _____ = _____   _____

TOTAL SCORE   _____

PLAYER 2   SCORE

Round 1: _____ + _____ + _____ = _____   _____

Round 2: _____ + _____ + _____ = _____   _____

Round 3: _____ + _____ + _____ = _____   _____

Round 4: _____ + _____ + _____ = _____   _____

Round 5: _____ + _____ + _____ = _____   _____

TOTAL SCORE   _____

Close to 20 Score Sheet

PLAYER 1   SCORE

Round 1: _____ + _____ + _____ = _____   _____

Round 2: _____ + _____ + _____ = _____   _____

Round 3: _____ + _____ + _____ = _____   _____

Round 4: _____ + _____ + _____ = _____   _____

Round 5: _____ + _____ + _____ = _____   _____

TOTAL SCORE   _____

PLAYER 2   SCORE

Round 1: _____ + _____ + _____ = _____   _____

Round 2: _____ + _____ + _____ = _____   _____

Round 3: _____ + _____ + _____ = _____   _____

Round 4: _____ + _____ + _____ = _____   _____

Round 5: _____ + _____ + _____ = _____   _____

TOTAL SCORE   _____

0	0	0	0
1	1	1	1
2	2	2	2

Practice Page
Putting Together and Taking Apart

3	3	3	3
4	4	4	4
5	5	5	5

Practice Page
Putting Together and Taking Apart

6	6	6	6
7	7	7	7
8	8	8	8

Practice Page
Putting Together and Taking Apart

9	9	9	9

10	10	10	10

Wild Card	Wild Card	Wild Card	Wild Card

Practice Page
Putting Together and Taking Apart

Practice Page A

There are _____ students in our class.

We have 40 cups for water.

Are there enough for the class? _____

How many leftovers will we have? _____

Explain how you figured this out. You can use numbers, words, or pictures.

Practice Page B

There are _____ students in our class.

We have 31 rulers.

Are there enough for the class? _____

How many leftovers will we have? _____

Explain how you figured this out. You can use numbers, words, or pictures.

Practice Page C

There are 10 legs in this group.
There are 4 heads in this group.
There are 8 ears in this group.
There are 30 fingers in this group.
There is 1 tail in this group.

Who could be in this group?

Show how you solved this problem. You can
use numbers, words, or pictures.

Practice Page D

There are 12 legs in this group.
There are 4 heads in this group.
There are 8 ears in this group.
There are 20 fingers in this group
There are 2 tails in this group.

Who could be in this group?

Show how you solved this problem. You can
use numbers, words, or pictures.